For my little one.

Mummy's Going to
the Hospital

ISBN 978-0-9994628-1-2

Library of Congress Control Number 1-5318989361

Published by
HomeCooked Entertainment
Los Angeles, CA

*Mummy went to the doctor,
and was told she has an
ouchy deep inside her body.*

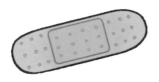

Now Mummy has to go
to the hospital, so that
the doctor can make her
ouchy better.

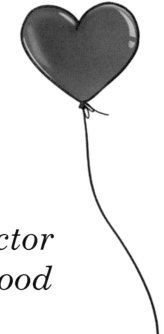

At the hospital, the doctor and nurses will take good care of Mummy.

Mummy will be thinking of you, even when she's sleeping.

You might miss Mummy,
and it might make you sad
to not see her.

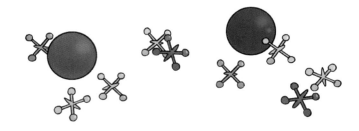

*It might make you angry
that Mummy isn't there
to play with you.*

But Mummy will be back soon, and when she comes home she'll show you her ouchy.

Mummy will need lots of rest, and it might worry you to see her sleeping so much.

*But every day
she'll get stronger.*

And stronger...

And before you know it,
Mummy's ouchy will be
all better!

Printed in Great Britain
by Amazon